The

Old Wo

who lived in a

Vinegar Bottle

a play by
Kathy Henderson

Illustrated by
Colin King

This play is based on a traditional story. It's the kind of story that different people have told each other at different times in different places for many, many years. The kind of story that starts "Once upon a time ..." and maybe gives us some advice about living as well.

For this reason one of the main characters in the play is the storyteller or **Narrator**. At the beginning of the play he or she stands in front of and just to one side of the main stage. The Narrator starts us off with "Once upon a time ..." and stays there all the way through to tell us what happens next.

The other main characters are:

The Old Woman

She's never happy with what she's got and always wants something better. She's very good at complaining.

Her Dog

He's an easy-going sort and though he doesn't like change much he always manages to find something to enjoy, in the end.

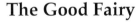

The Good Fairy

Well, she's just a very "good" fairy. She wants to make things right and make people happy. She's smiley and kind and talks in a sweet sing-song voice. But even she has her limits.

There are also small parts for a **Servant** and a **Royal Secretary**.

The
Old Woman
who lived in a
Vinegar Bottle

Scene One
Outside a large vinegar bottle.

Cast
Narrator
Dog
Old Woman
Good Fairy

Narrator: Once upon a time there was an old woman who lived in a vinegar bottle.

Dog: (*Interrupting*) With her dog!

Narrator: As I was saying, there was an old woman *and her dog* who lived in a vinegar bottle.

Dog: (*Interrupting again*) And a very nice vinegar bottle it is. I won't hear a word against it. Look, it's got strong glass walls to keep the weather out, a good view from the top and smooth round curves for me to curl up against when I want to go to sleep. It's cosy.

Old Woman: It's smelly!

Dog: Snug.

Old Woman: Cramped!

Dog: It's home.

Old Woman: It's a scandal! Nobody should have to live in a vinegar bottle, least of all ME! I deserve better, *much* better.

Narrator: Well, one day, a good fairy was passing by ...

(Enter Good Fairy, smiling sweetly.)

Dog: *(Noticing her)* Woof! Woof!

Old Woman: *(Not noticing her)* Oh, do be quiet, Fido!

Narrator: She heard the Old Woman grumbling.

Old Woman: It's a shame! It's rotten! It's a scandal!

Good Fairy: *(In a sweet, sing-song voice)*
Flitter, flutter, what's the matter?
Maybe I can make it better.

Old Woman: *(Noticing the Fairy at last)* It's this bottle.
It's a shame. It's a scandal. It really is.
I shouldn't have to live in a smelly old
vinegar bottle! *I* should live in a nice little
cottage with a thatched roof and roses
growing round the door. That's where *I*
should live.

7

Good Fairy: Very well …

(The Good Fairy takes up her "magic spell" position, like a ballet dancer: one leg in the air, arms out, wand held high. She speaks in the sweet sing-song voice.)

Good Fairy: When you go to bed tonight
Shut the doors, put out the light,
Close your eyes, count one, two, three
And you shall see what you shall see.

Narrator: So the Old Woman went to bed,
closed her eyes, counted one, two, three
and … fell fast asleep.
But in the morning …

Scene Two

Outside a pretty little thatched cottage with roses round the door.

Cast

Dog

Old Woman

Narrator

Dog: *(Very cross)* Woof! Woof! Grrrr!
What's all this? Where am I?
Where's my nice cosy home gone?

Old Woman: Do be quiet, Fido!

(She looks around.)

Old Woman: Well now, isn't this lovely? What a pretty little cottage! Look at the thatch. Look at the neat little windows. Look at those lovely pink roses growing round the door! Oh yes, this is a much nicer place to live than a vinegar bottle. This is *wonderful!*

Narrator: But she quite forgot to thank the Fairy.

Dog: Typical!

Everyone : *(Except the Old Woman)* Tst! Tst! Tst!

Scene Three
Outside the cottage.

Cast
Narrator
Good Fairy
Old Woman
Dog

Narrator: The Good Fairy went North and she went South and she went East and she went West, all about the business she had to do, until one day she thought to herself …

Good Fairy: Goodness me,
It's time I went
To see if the Old Woman
And her dog are content.

Narrator: And off she went towards the little thatched cottage. But, as she got nearer, what did she hear?

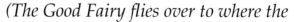

*(The Good Fairy flies over to where the
Old Woman is stamping around outside the cottage,
while the dog gnaws a bone on the doorstep.)*

Old Woman: Pink roses, blooming pink roses!
If I see another pink rose I shall scream!

Good Fairy: Goodness gracious!
Well I never!
You could knock me
Down with a feather.

Old Woman: And just look at that thatch!
And those tiny windows!
This poky little cottage is
going to drive me crazy!

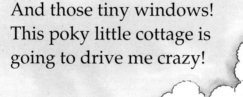

Dog: *(Looking up from his bone)* It's not so bad, really. It's got some quite good corners once you get used to it.

Old Woman: What do *you* know about these things? You're only a dog. It may be good enough for you but it's *not* good enough for *me!* *I* deserve something *much* better.

Good Fairy: *(To the Old Woman and the Dog)*
Oh dear, oh dear!
Is something wrong?
Do let me help.
It won't take long.

Old Woman: It's a shame. It's a scandal! *I* shouldn't
have to live in a poky little place like this.
I should be living in a grand town house,
four storeys high, with servants to wait on me
and a car with a driver to take me to visit the
Queen. That's where *I* should live!

Good Fairy: *(Surprised)* Very well.

(She takes up her magic spell pose and speaks in the sing-song voice.)

Good Fairy: When you go to bed tonight
Shut the doors, put out the light,
Close your eyes, count one, two, three
And you shall see what you shall see.

Narrator: So the Old Woman went to bed. She closed her eyes, counted one, two, three and ... fell fast asleep again.
But in the morning ...

Scene Four
Inside the smart bedroom of a grand town house.

Cast
Dog

Old Woman

Servant

Narrator

Dog: *(Opening one eye)* GRRR! Not again! Now where am I? A dog doesn't know if he's coming or going these days!

Old Woman: *(Sitting up in bed and looking around her happily)* Stop fussing, Fido!

Dog: *(To himself)* Ooh, isn't she bossy! If you ask me, she's getting too big for her boots.

Old Woman: Silence!

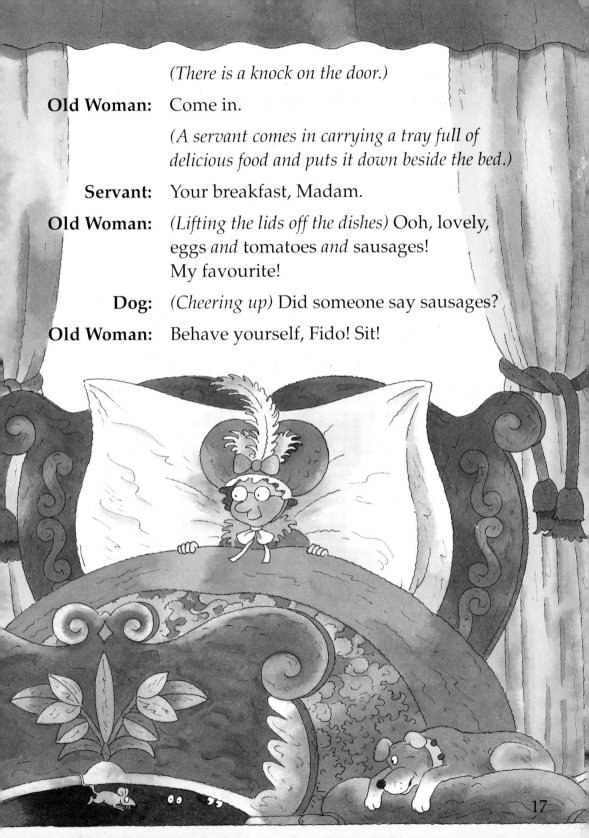

(There is a knock on the door.)

Old Woman: Come in.

(A servant comes in carrying a tray full of delicious food and puts it down beside the bed.)

Servant: Your breakfast, Madam.

Old Woman: *(Lifting the lids off the dishes)* Ooh, lovely, eggs *and* tomatoes *and* sausages! My favourite!

Dog: *(Cheering up)* Did someone say sausages?

Old Woman: Behave yourself, Fido! Sit!

Servant:	Shall I take the hound away, Madam?
Dog:	"Hound" indeed!
Old Woman:	Yes. Put him in the kitchen, I think.
Dog:	What?! Me?! Pushed around by some servant? I don't believe this!
Old Woman:	*(Ignoring the Dog)* Now what am I doing today?
Servant:	*(Opens notebook)* Your new clothes have arrived from the dressmaker, Madam, and the hairdresser will be here at ten o'clock.
Old Woman:	Oh good. And then?
Servant:	The car will call at twelve o'clock to take you to the palace for lunch with the Queen.
Old Woman:	Good. Good. And then?
Servant:	You have an invitation for tea with Lord Busybody and another for dinner with the Duchess of Smarm. Will that be all for now, Madam?
Old Woman:	*(Smiling)* Yes, thank you.

(The servant leaves, dragging the Dog with him.)

Dog: Hey, let go of me! Get your hands off! Grrrrr!

(The servant closes the door behind them. The Old Woman smiles and lies back in her huge bed munching a sausage.)

Old Woman: Oh, this is more like it. This is wonderful. This is just what I wanted. I'm really very pleased.

Narrator: But she quite forgot to thank the Fairy.

Everyone: *(Except the Old Woman)* Tst! Tst! Tst!

Scene Five

In the drawing room of the town house.

Cast
Narrator
Good Fairy
Old Woman
Dog

Narrator: Well, the Good Fairy went North and she went South and she went East and she went West, all about the business she had to do, until one day she thought to herself ...

Good Fairy: Gracious! I must fly along
And see how the Old Woman
And her dog are getting on!

Narrator: And off she went to the grand town house. But as she flew into the grand drawing room, what did she hear?

20

(The Good Fairy flies over to where the Old Woman is pacing up and down the town house drawing room, grumbling. The Dog is lying on one of the big soft sofas, happily gnawing an enormous bone.)

Old Woman: *(Crossly)* It won't do. It really won't do at all.

Good Fairy: Goodness me! Not happy yet?
How quickly people do forget!

Old Woman: This place is just too terribly ordinary for words.

Dog: *(Nearly choking on his bone)* Ordinary! Ordinary?! If this is ordinary I must be dreaming!

Old Woman: Silence, you! No, it's not good enough. Only one little house ...

Dog: Little!

Old Woman: Only fifteen rooms, twelve servants and three cars *and* I even have to curtsey to the Queen like any old duchess. No, *I* deserve better, *much* better.

Good Fairy: *(Surprised)* Is there something I can do? Let me make your dream come true.

Old Woman: Ah, Fairy. I'm glad to see you. Yes. This is a shame. It's a scandal! *I* shouldn't have to live in this ordinary little house. *I* should be living in a palace, a huge royal palace with another three spare for the holidays and lots and lots of servants and cars and horses and dogs ...

Dog: What?!

Old Woman: ... and an aeroplane and a private helicopter and a yacht, no, two yachts and ...

Good Fairy: *(Interrupts her)* Very well …
Hold your peace and never fear.
I think I've just about got the idea!

(Takes up her magic spell pose and speaks in the sweet sing-song voice again.)

Good Fairy: When you go to bed tonight
Shut the doors, put out the light,
Close your eyes, count one, two, three
And you shall see what you shall see.

Narrator: So the Old Woman went to bed. She
closed her eyes, counted one, two, three
and … fell fast asleep as usual.
But in the morning …

Scene Six
Inside the royal bedroom.

Cast
Old Woman
Royal Secretary
Dog
Narrator

(A trumpeter sounds a fanfare. A row of royal footmen in red and gold uniforms enter, bringing breakfast, the newspapers and the royal dogs.)

Old Woman:	*(Sitting up and rubbing her eyes)* Oh, good heavens!
Royal Secretary:	Good morning, Your Majesty.
Old Woman:	Oh, er ... yes. Good morning ... my subjects.
Dog:	Grrrrrrrr!
Old Woman:	Why, Fido! You do look funny in that gold-studded collar and that lead.

Dog: You can laugh! It's all right for you! I've never been tied up in my life. Now I can't move and there are corgis everywhere! Grrrrr!

Old Woman: *(Ignoring him and turning to the servants)* What are our plans for today?

Royal Secretary: *(Bowing)* This morning, Ma'am, the Prime Minister will be popping in for a chat.
At noon your favourite horse, Moneymaker, will be running in the Royal Races.
At tea-time the King of Umpopo begins his state visit to Your Majesty. And for dinner you will be joined by the Prince and Princess of Snails and the President of the Untidy States at a state banquet.

Old Woman: I see. Very good. *(She smiles.)* We are pleased. We are very, very pleased.

Dog: *(Crossly)* Speak for yourself! I expect I'm going to be shut in the royal kennels all day.

Old Woman: In fact, we are simply delighted!

Narrator: And she ordered everyone around all over the place, but ...
she quite forgot to thank the Fairy.

Everyone: *(Except the Old Woman)* Tst! Tst! Tst!

Scene Seven
The royal throne room.

Cast
Narrator
Good Fairy
Old Woman
Dog

Narrator: So the Good Fairy went North and she went
South and she went East and she went West,
all about the business she had to do,
until one day she thought to herself ...

Good Fairy: Goodness me!
How time flies past!
Surely the Old Woman
Is happy at last.

Narrator: And off she went towards the royal palace.
But as she got nearer, what did she hear?

27

(The Good Fairy flies over to where the Old Woman, wearing her crown and royal robes, is sitting on the throne in the royal throne room. She's in a very bad temper and stamping her foot. The Dog is sitting a safe distance away.)

Good Fairy: Let me see. Oh no! What's this?
Here's a scene I'd gladly miss.

Old Woman: We are *not* happy. We are definitely
NOT happy!

Dog: Speak for yourself. We royal dogs are
all right. Roast venison for dinner last night.
(He licks his lips.)

Old Woman: Silence, you! No. It simply isn't good enough!
Only *one* little country to rule over?
Someone like ourself deserves better,
much better.

Dog: *(Noticing the Fairy)* Oh, it's you again.
I wouldn't listen to her if I were you.
She's off her head.

Old Woman: No, *we* should rule over France as well as
Britain. In fact we should probably rule over
the whole of Europe. And why stop there?
Why not Africa, Asia and the Americas too?

Good Fairy: Still not happy? Oh dear me!
Can I help? Try me and see.

Old Woman: Ah you, Fairy. There you are.
Kiss my hand.

(The Good Fairy looks cross.)

Old Woman: It's a shame. It's a scandal. A great ruler
like ourself should not just be ruling over one
country, *we* should be ruling the whole world,
do you hear? Arrange it at once, please!

Good Fairy: Are you quite sure?

Old Woman: How dare you question me?!
Now do what you're told. This instant!

Good Fairy: *(Not at all pleased)* Very well.

(She takes up the magic spell pose and puts on a rather cross but still sweet sing-song voice.)

Good Fairy: When you go to bed tonight
Shut the doors, put out the light,
Close your eyes, count one, two, three
(Very slowly) And you shall see ...
What you shall see.

Narrator: So the Old Woman went to her
fine royal bed with the velvet cover
and the six feather mattresses. She closed
her eyes, counted one, two, three
and ... fell fast asleep.
And in the morning ...

Scene Eight
Outside the vinegar bottle.

Cast
Narrator
Dog
Old Woman

Narrator: There she was, back in her vinegar bottle again.

Dog: *(Relieved)* At last! Home sweet home!

Old Woman: *(Furious and spluttering)* But ... But ... But ... This is outrageous! This is unreasonable! It's a shame. It's a scandal! *Me?* In a vinegar bottle?! I don't believe it! Wait till I get my hands on that blooming Fairy!

(The curtain falls as she's speaking.)

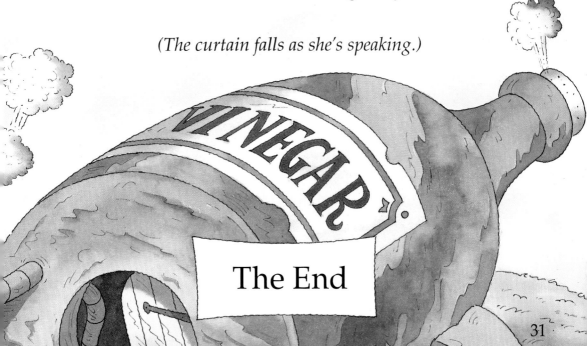

The End